Copyright © 2022 Our Ancestories

Book illustrations by Simbarashe Langton Vera and Anastasia Kyrpenko

Cover art and illustrations by Simbarashe Langton Vera and Hossein Kalantari

Digital color by Onder Tur

Map design by Mats Wedin

Book design by Dania Zafar

Research assistance by Marianela Parodi

Edited by Mary Blake, Liz Tichelaar, Shamontiel Vaughn, and Brooke Vitale

Pronunciations by Engy Hedayat

ISBN: 978-1-7771179-9-3 (Hardcover)

First printing edition 2022

www.our-ancestories.com

contact@our-ancestories.com

We acknowledge the support of the Canada Council for the Arts.

Canada Council   Conseil des arts
for the Arts   du Canada

THIS BOOK BELONGS TO:

_____

The history of Africa is rich, diverse, and full of countless stories, characters, and encounters.

The region we now call Egypt played an important role in the development of African history, science, and culture.

However, there is more to Egypt's history than is generally understood.

The country's many mysteries have given rise to an abundance of theories about its beginnings, including how the pyramids were created. This book combines many months of research with engaging illustrations and simple language to make Egypt's past easy to understand.

Together, you and I will go back 5,000 years in time to a period when the world was a lot different than it is today. You will be introduced to a multi-talented genius named Imhotep who changed history forever.

Enjoy!

Ekiuwa Aire

Our Ancestories

IMHOTEP
OF ANCIENT KEMET

WRITTEN BY
EKIUWA AIRE

VOCABULARY GUIDE

Bas reliefs (bahs ruh·leefs)—Flat but slightly three-dimensional carvings or sculptures. For example, a coin is a bas relief.

Djoser (jow·sah)—Egyptian king from the 3rd Dynasty who ruled around 2686–2648 BC.

Imhotep (ee·mow·tep)—A genius who changed the land of Kemet. His name means "he who comes in peace."

Kanofer (kha·neh·fir)—Imhotep's dad, a famous architect and master builder.

Kemet (keh·muht)—Egypt was called Kemet in ancient times. Kemet means "the black land."

Kheredouankh (kreh·dou·ank)—Imhotep's mom, an educated woman.

Khnum (kha·noom)—One of Egypt's earliest gods who had power over the Nile River and could cause it to flood.

Mastaba (muh·staa·buh)—Early versions of pyramids. These were more rectangular in shape.

Papyrus (puh·pai·ruhs)—The plant used to make paper.

Ptah (tah)—An Egyptian creator god who is believed to have created the world by the sheer force of his will.

Pyramid (pee·ruh·mid)—A big stone building with triangular sides that meet together at a point; they were made to bury Egyptian kings in.

Quarrying (kworr·ee·ing)—The cutting of stones to use for building materials.

Ra (rah)—The Egyptian sun god, who some Egyptians thought created the world.

Scribe (skribe)—A person who writes things down.

Vizier (vuh·zeer)—An Arabic word meaning a high-ranking political advisor or the king's closest adviser.

Long ago in the ancient city of **Memphis**, Kemet, lived a little boy named Imhotep. From birth, Imhotep was loved very much by his mom Kheredouankh and his dad Kanofer, a famous builder.

Imhotep was a curious and smart boy.
He questioned everything.

What makes the papyrus plant grow so tall?
Who paints the lotus flower white, pink, or blue?
How do gazelles run and falcons fly?
Dogs bark, but why do cats meow?

What makes rain fill the mighty Nile River?
How do the sun and stars get to the sky?

Imhotep's parents told him the sun god Ra created
everything, including people. Still, he had more questions.

As he grew, Imhotep became interested in his dad's work. One day, Imhotep noticed some workers making bricks from the mud of the Nile River.

"Dad, what will you make with all those bricks?" asked Imhotep.

"These bricks will make a mighty mastaba," said Kanofer.

"What is a mastaba?" asked Imhotep.

"A mastaba is a house of eternity," Kanofer explained. "The king's body will be placed in it for safekeeping after his death. This building will be my most important work."

Imhotep wanted to follow in his dad's footsteps.

He started building little mastabas of his own.
Since he had no bricks, he used what he could find.
Imhotep found that reeds and mud worked great to
build the walls.

He made mastabas of all different sizes. Then, he
stacked them, with the largest on the bottom and the
smallest on the top.

"What are you doing?" asked Kanofer.

"I'm building mastabas, like you," replied Imhotep.

"But why are you stacking them?" he asked.

"I like them that way," said Imhotep. "The higher the stack, the grander the eternal house!"

Imhotep thought deeply about his next question.

"How long do mud bricks last, Dad?" asked Imhotep.

"If properly taken care of, they can last up to 300 years," replied Kanofer.

"Three hundred years is a long time," reasoned Imhotep. "But that is not forever. I wonder if there is something stronger than mud bricks."

Soon, Imhotep's friends noticed that he was different. They began to bring him their questions. He became known for being quite wise. Everyone was in awe of Imhotep.

As he grew, Imhotep's remarkable wisdom grew too. Like other kids his age, Imhotep went to a school called the House of Life. There, he learned to be a priest and a scribe.

Priests in Kemet followed various career paths. Some became doctors, others scientists, and others architects.

Imhotep's curiosity was so great that he explored many paths at the same time.

His thirst for knowledge spread far and wide, finally reaching even King Djoser!

King Djoser was so impressed by Imhotep that he made him High Priest to the sun god Ra at **Heliopolis**. Imhotep was to lead the people and their king in the practice of the Kemetic religion.

But all was not well in Kemet. Year after year, the mighty **Nile River** grew smaller and drier. It no longer flooded the land with water for the crops. The wheat and barley that fed the people and animals stopped growing. The herds of animals that provided meat and milk starved. This lasted for seven years. The people were desperate for food, water, and hope.

King Djoser turned to Imhotep for help. "Which god is holding back water from the land and why?" he wanted to know.

Imhotep studied the religious books and learned that the god Khnum ruled over the rivers and lakes.

Khnum's temple was located near the origin of the Nile in **Elephantine**. Imhotep traveled to the temple and found it to be in poor shape. *No wonder Khnum is angry,* he thought.

He returned to King Djoser and informed him of his discovery.

"Khnum is holding back the waters because his temple is falling apart," he said. "We must clean it up. Perhaps we can grow fruits in the field and use the profits to fix the temple. Then Khnum will be happy."

King Djoser agreed. The temple was repaired. The Nile flooded again!

King Djoser was so pleased that he made Imhotep his vizier. Imhotep was now the king's right-hand man and top advisor.

Once prosperity returned to the land, King Djoser began to plan his own royal tomb. Every king must have one, after all. As vizier, Imhotep's job included overseeing Kemet's building program. He was to build the king's mastaba in **Sakkara**.

Imhotep went to work right away. He remembered the mastabas he made of reeds and mud when he was younger. Imhotep wanted to build King Djoser's tomb of stacked mastabas too. To make it last forever, he used limestone instead of clay bricks.

"Your tomb will be grander and more beautiful than any that has come before," he told King Djoser. "It won't be just another mastaba, but a divine palace for your eternal rest. Everyone who sees it will remember the great King Djoser."

Building King Djoser's tomb palace required the quarrying,
transportation, shaping, and precise placement of heavy blocks of stone.
New tools and processes were necessary, along with thousands of workers.
Imhotep directed everything.

When it was completed, Imhotep's stacked mastabas were amazing. The building's shape, broad at the bottom and narrower at the top, was quite unique. It formed the very first pyramid!

Beneath the pyramid ran a maze of tunnels to confuse anyone who wanted to disturb the king's eternal rest.

Imhotep changed the way tombs were built in what is now known as **Egypt**. The step pyramid he built for King Djoser still stands today. His work led the way for other builders. Because of Imhotep, we have the famous pyramids of **Giza**.

PRIEST

SCULPTOR

SCIENTIST

POLITICIAN

But Imhotep didn't stop there.

He was a polymath, meaning he excelled at many things.

SCRIBE

PHILOSOPHER

ARCHITECT

DOCTOR

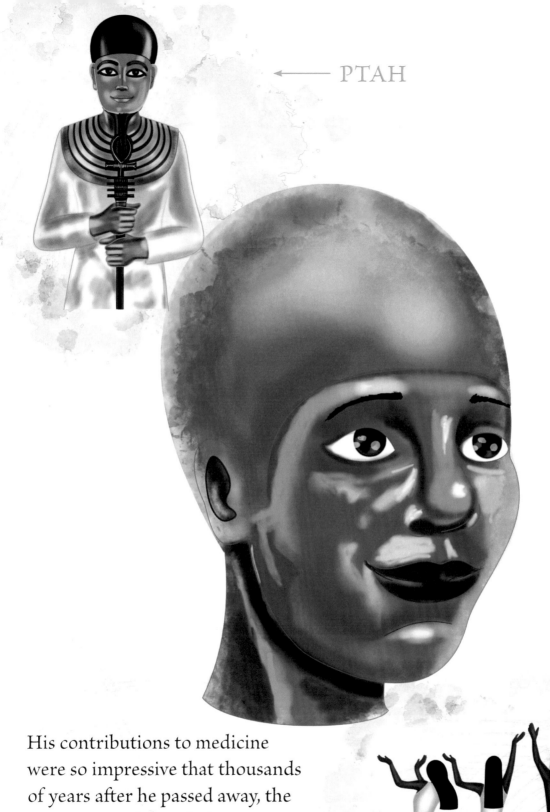

PTAH

His contributions to medicine were so impressive that thousands of years after he passed away, the Egyptians and Greeks began to worship him as a god of medicine and the son of the god Ptah.

He is still admired today every time someone visits the pyramids.

Nobody knows where Imhotep is buried. Perhaps one day, if you have the curiosity and determination of Imhotep, you will be the one to discover where.

IMHOTEP AND HIS ACCOMPLISHMENTS

1. **Improved Egyptian civilization.**

Imhotep, during his time as a vizier, helped to bring important improvements to Egyptian civilization:

- The technique of building with stones was developed.

- The first pyramid in Egypt was built, indicating the beginning of the pyramid age.

- Sculptures and bas reliefs marked an important turning point in the evolution of Egyptian art.

- Possibly the oldest dam in the world, the Sadd el-Kafara near Helwan was planned and constructed.

In 1926, archaeologists found a statue of King Djoser in Sakkara. On this statue, Imhotep was called:

- Chancellor of the King of Lower Egypt

- First after the King of Upper Egypt

- Administrator of the Great Mansion

- Hereditary Noble

- High Priest of Heliopolis

2. Founded Egyptian medicine

- He conducted research to understand the causes of various illnesses. He then used herbs he grew to find remedies for these illnesses.

- He was one of the first doctors to write down how he treated his patients. Some scholars believe he contributed to a book called the Edwin Smith Papyrus, which contained 48 different injuries and how to heal them.

3. Introduced the construction of stone columns

- He was the first to carve stone columns that looked like bundled reeds and other plants.

- He thought of placing columns close together to carry the weight of heavy roofs and beams. This allowed people to have taller, more spacious houses.

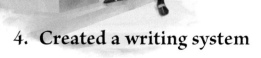

4. Created a writing system

- During Djoser's reign, the writing system was reformed. For the first time, a continuous text was created in hieroglyphs.

EGYPT'S HISTORY

To understand Egypt's history, we have to go back thousands of years before the Egyptians were called Egyptians.

Human civilization developed in Africa. In fact, the oldest human bones in the world have been found in **Ethiopia's** Kibish and Morocco's Jebel Irhoud.

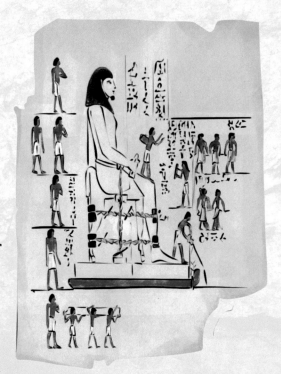

Scholars believe that two groups of the first African humans dispersed and settled all over the world.

The first group followed a Northern route and settled in Arabia, South Asia, and the Levant (**Lebanon, Syria, Iraq, Palestine,** and **Jordan**).

The second group stayed in Africa and migrated southward along the coast spreading rapidly out of **Nubia**, East Africa.

Ancient Nubia was a nation, which in 5000 BC, began to domesticate sheep, goats, and cattle as the Sahara Desert became drier.

People eventually settled in the valley of the Nile River for thousands of years.

The Nile River is the longest river in the world. It flows through northeast Africa for about 4,132 miles (6,650 kilometers).

The most distant sources of the Nile are rivers that begin in **Burundi** and **Rwanda**. Those rivers flow into **Lake Victoria**. From Lake Victoria, the Nile flows through **Uganda**, **South Sudan**, and **Sudan**. For about 500 miles (800 kilometers) in South Sudan and Sudan, the river is called the **White Nile**.

The White Nile is joined by the **Blue Nile** in the city of Khartoum, Sudan. The Nile continues to flow north across the deserts of Sudan and Egypt.

North of **Cairo**, Egypt, the Nile enters the region called the Nile Valley where the Nile River spreads out and drains into the Mediterranean Sea.

At first, the people who lived in the Nile Valley were people who moved north from Nubia (Ethiopia/Sudan). Later on, others also moved east (from **Libya**) to the Nile Valley to escape the ever-drying Sahara. Later still, people from the Middle East moved to the Nile Valley too.

The Nile Valley was good for farming because it got lots of water from the Nile River, and the weather made it easy to grow plants and raise animals.

During the Early Dynastic Period and part of the Old Kingdom, Egypt was called Kemet. Kemet was in the Nile Valley region. The beginning of Kemet is around 3100 BC.

The people of Kemet were industrious. They invented many things such as medicine, musical instruments, paper, pens, and writing. They believed cats brought them good luck. They made clothes out of white linen, and kids wore a single, long braid or lock of hair on one side.

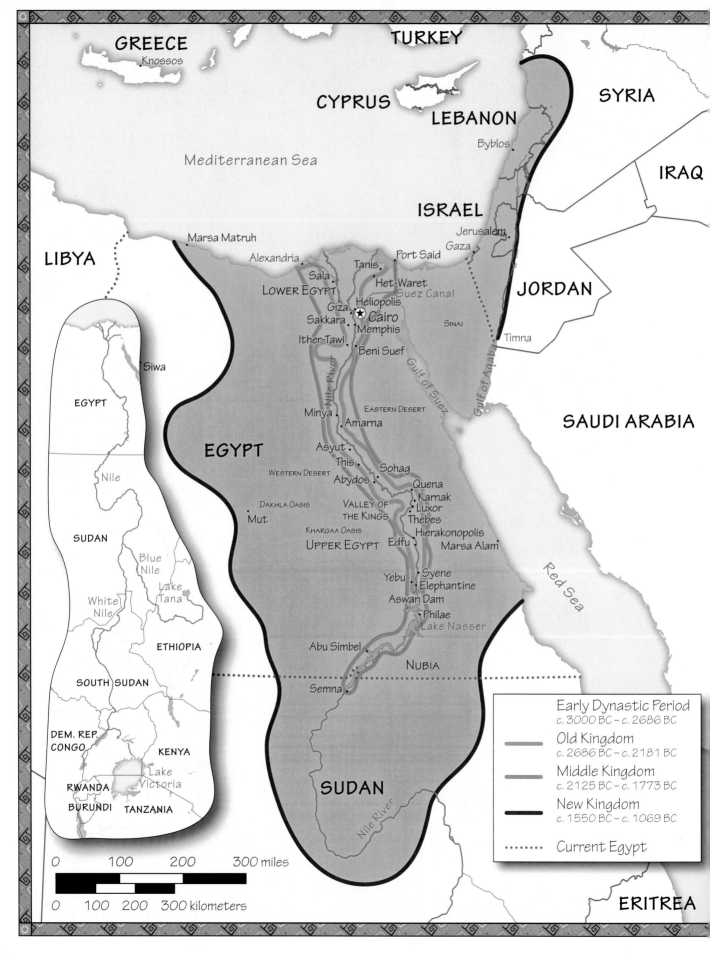

ABOUT THE AUTHOR

Ekiuwa Aire is an award-winning author and speaker born and raised in Benin City, Edo, Nigeria. She is passionate about sharing positive stories on African history with children.

She lives with her husband and two daughters in Ontario, Canada.

ABOUT THE ILLUSTRATORS

Simbarashe Langton Vera is a self-taught Zimbabwean artist who is passionate about illustrating and exploring his creativity. He has worked on numerous projects ranging from comics to children's books and his motivation is his family.

Anastasia Kyrpenko graduated with a BA in visual arts from the American University of Athens, Greece. She has since been using her creativity to support change. She works in the fields of visual art, digital collages, motion design, and illustration.

ACTIVITIES YOU CAN ENJOY WITH THIS BOOK

When you read this book, look out for red text in the story. Can you find these locations on the map provided?

Can you find Imhotep's cat on all the pages in the story up to where he becomes the vizier?

The end pages include hieroglyphs that were used as references for some of the book's illustrations. Can you match the hieroglyphs to their illustrations? What else do you notice about the end pages?

GET THE COLLECTION!

OTHER BOOKS IN THE "OUR ANCESTORIES" LINEUP

References

- A. Beyin, "Upper Pleistocene Human Dispersals out of Africa: A Review of the Current State of the Debate," Int. J. Evol. Biol., vol. 615094, pp. 1–17, Jan. 2011, doi: 10.4061/2011/615094.

- A. G. Hilliard, "The Meaning of KMT (Ancient Egyptian) History for Contemporary African American Experience," Phylon (1960), vol. 49, no. 1/2, pp. 10–22, Feb. 1992, doi: 10.2307/3132613.

- C. A. Diop, "Pigmentation of the Ancient Egyptians: Test by Melanin Analysis," Bull. L'institute Fondam. D'afrique noire, vol. XXXV, no. 3, pp. 515–30, 1973.

- C. Diop, "Origin of the ancient Egyptians," in General History of Africa II, 1981.

- Forbes, R. J. (1940). Imhotep. SAGE Publications.

- Gunn, B. (1926). Inscriptions from the Step-Pyramid Site. Ann. Dui Service Anttiq., 26, 192–195.

- Hurry, J. B. (1926). Imhotep: The vizier and physician of King Zoser and afterwards the Egyptian god of medicine. Oxford University Press, Inc.

  Kahl, J. (2001). [Old Kingdom]. Third Dynasty.

- Luth, V. P. (1963). Imhotep Oder Asklepios: On the beginning of scientific medicine in Egypt and Greece. Hippocrate, 34.

- Magli, G. (2009). Geometry and perspective in the landscape of the Saqqara pyramids. History and Philosophy of Physics.

- Miller, D., & Brandon, S. G. F. (2014). Beliefs, Rituals, and Symbols of Ancient Egypt, Mesopotamia, and the Fertile Crescent (Man, Myth, and Magic). Cavendish Square.

- N Saleem, S. (2021). Egyptian Medical Civilization: from Dawn of History to Kasr Al Ainy School.

- Osler, W. (2004). The Evolution of Modern Medicine. Kessinger Publishing.

- Ostrin, S. (2002). Imhotep ... First, Last, and Always. Bulletin of Anesthesia History, 20, 1,4-5. https://doi.org/10.1016/S1522-8649(02)50046-9

- S. Keita, "Exploring Northeast African metric craniofacial variation at the individual level: A comparative study using principal components analysis," Am. J. Hum. Biol., vol. 16, pp. 679–689, Nov. 2004, doi: 10.1002/ajhb.20076.

- S. Zakrzewski, "Population Continuity or Population Change: Formation of the Ancient Egyptian State," Am. J. Phys. Anthropol., vol. 132, pp. 501–509, Apr. 2007, doi: 10.1002/ajpa.20569.

- Short, B. (2009). Imhotep and the Origins of Ancient Egyptian Military Medicine. ADF Health, 10(1), 48–50.

- van Middendorp, J. J., Sanchez, G. M., & Burridge, A. L. (2010). The Edwin Smith papyrus: a clinical reappraisal of the oldest known document on spinal injuries. European Spine Journal : Official Publication of the European Spine Society, the European Spinal Deformity Society, and the European Section of the Cervical Spine Research Society, 19(11), 1815–1823. https://doi.org/10.1007/s00586-010-1523-6

- W. Petrie, Prehistoric Egypt. London: Bernard Quaritch, 1920.

- Zimmerman, M. (2018). Practicing Medicine in Ancient Egypt. Juniata Voices, 144–152.

Subject Matter Experts Consulted

- Lance Stephens AKA HakatRe
- Engy Hedayat, Egyptologist
- Nicole Hansen, Ph.D. (Near Eastern Language and Civilizations)
- Jared Krebsbach, Ph.D. (History)

Fact Check: Imhotep is shown wearing a red robe in his later years. This is based on a popular hieroglyph used in reference to Imhotep. However, there is no proof that this is the true image of Imhotep. The most popularly accepted representation of Imhotep is the statue, where he is represented as a seated scribe, holding a papyrus.